Volume 2 Reading Skills Progress Chart

Have the child complete this survey of phonetic reading skills. Complete the survey periodically, tracking the child's progress by tabulating and recording the results at the bottom of the page.

Vowels (The Five Power Letters)
Point to the vowels and tell their long and short sounds.
(1 point for each vowel letter and its two sounds = 10 total points)

Digraphs
What sound does each digraph make? One of them makes two different sounds. (2 points each sound = 8 total points)

e v i o n u f a	ch th wh sh

One-Vowel Families
Read each of the following vowel families in boxes 1, 2, and 3.
(1 point for each family = 15 total points possible

Two-Vowel Families

Consonant-Vowel Families
Long or short sounds are acceptable.

Using the Reading Clues
Use the Reading Clues to read the words in the fourth box.
(2 points each = 10 total points possible)

①	②	③	④
ab	eet	ba	lane
em	ave	ve	bed
id	ipe	ti	rope
ot	ute	ro	fun
ug	oat	nu	hide

Sight Words
Read each of the following sight words. (2 points each = 12 points total)

my	a	here	is	no	the

Capital Letters
These are the most difficult capital letters to remember. What are the names and sounds for each letter? (1 point for each letter and each sound = 20 total points)

A	B	D	E	G	H	I	L	Q	R

My Progress (75 possible)	Date:					
	Score:					

TIPS FOR THE PARENT

The following are instructions and a sample page for the review section. Dialogue is provided, but we encourage you to use your own words, praise, and humor.

Review

1 "What is this picture? A question mark? Yes! What sound does **question** begin with? **Quh!** You are so smart!"

2 "Can you find the letter that makes the **quh** sound? Let's try saying question mark with the beginning sounds in the box. Is it **question mark, pestion mark,** or **destion mark?** That's silly! Which letter do you think is right? The letter **q**? Very good! Let's circle the letter **q.** The letter **q** says **quh** as in **question mark.**"

3 Continue for each picture, moving from left to right.

4 After each review page, practice Beginning Sounds, Letters and Sounds, and Blending, with the My Alphabet Book and Beginning Sounds and Blending Cards.

Instructions for the page are written in the shaded box at the top. Read the instructions silently and then instruct the child.

This is the name of the picture.

This is the concept or skill for this page.

PRACTICE CARDS: The Parent Guide tells how to use the cards for teaching, for practicing, and for playing games.

Letters and Sounds
My Alphabet Book
Deck 2, **Letters and Sounds**

Deck 2

Blending
Deck 3, **One-Vowel Families**
Deck 5, **One-Vowel Words**
Deck 4, **Two-Vowel Families**
Deck 6, **Two-Vowel Words**

hhuumm

Deck 2

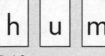

Deck 5

Deck 6

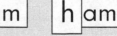
Decks 2 and 3

Decks 2 and 4

Let's review the beginning sounds of the alphabet letters. Name the picture. What sound does it start with? Trace the letter that makes that sound.

Sing the Alphabet Song with Miss Becky!

apple

starts with
ă sound

a

ball

starts with
buh sound

b

cat

starts with
c sound

c

dog

starts with
duh sound

d

elephant

starts with
ě sound

e

fish

starts with
fff sound

f

goat

starts with
guh sound

g

hat

starts with
h sound

h

Letters and Sounds

5

Continue the alphabet sounds. Name the picture. What sound does it start with? Trace the letter that makes that sound.

 icky

starts with
ĭ sound

i

 jet

starts with
juh sound

j

 kangaroo

starts with
k sound

k

 lollipop

starts with
lll sound

l

 monkey

starts with
mmm sound

m

 nose

starts with
nnn sound

n

 octopus

starts with
ŏ sound

o

 popcorn

starts with
p sound

p

 queen

starts with
quh sound

q

Let's review the beginning sounds of the alphabet letters. Name the picture. What sound does it start with? Trace the letter that makes that sound.

Sing the Alphabet Song with Miss Becky!

apple

starts with **ă** sound

ball

starts with **b**uh sound

cat

starts with **c** sound

dog

starts with **d**uh sound

elephant

starts with **ĕ** sound

fish

starts with **fff** sound

goat

starts with **g**uh sound

hat

starts with **h** sound

Letters and Sounds

Continue the alphabet sounds. Name the picture. What sound does it start with? Trace the letter that makes that sound.

icky

starts with
ĭ sound

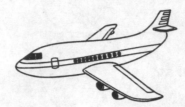

jet

starts with
j**uh** sound

kangaroo

starts with
k sound

lollipop

starts with
lll sound

monkey

starts with
mmm sound

nose

starts with
nnn sound

octopus

starts with
ŏ sound

popcorn

starts with
p sound

queen

starts with
q**uh** sound

Challenger Phonics Fun!®

Volume 2 Vowels and Reading

Activity and Reading Book

USING the VOLUME 2 ACTIVITY BOOK

TO THE PARENT

"Tips for the Parent" pages are located in the activity book where major skills and concepts are introduced.

The parent will need to determine how much help to give your child. Some students will need constant, detailed guidance, while others may be able to work quickly through the activity book with little assistance.

Before beginning the activity book, both parent and child should become familiar with the video and the songs within the video. Words to the songs are in this book.

Establish reading patterns wherever possible. Starting the in the upper left-hand corner of the page, point to the words to the songs and continue from left to right. While reading to the child, call attention to the pertinent Challenger Phonics Fun reading skills and concepts.

Remember to praise your child's efforts, to encourage independent thinking, and to have fun! The true joy of learning and ultimately self worth are derived through personal achievement.

Even though the skills in Volume 1 are reviewed, before starting the Volume 2 Activity and Reading Book, make sure your child can demonstrate competency with the following skills:

1) Be able to identify the beginning sounds to spoken words and pictures.

Ball starts with **b**uh.

2) Be able to identify all 26 letters and their sounds.

Letter **b** says "**b**uh."

3) Demonstrate that he or she understands how letters are blended together to form short words.

H-u-m says "*hum*."

If the student is not comfortable with the three skills listed above, return to Volume 1 and practice until the student is fluent with them.

CONCEPTS and SKILLS in VOLUME 2

- **Volume 2 Reading Skills Progress Chart**
- **Review Volume 1 Skills**
  Beginning sounds and Letter Sounds
  Blending one-vowel words
- **The Vowels, Long and Short Sounds**
- **One-Vowel Rule** (Short Vowels) **and One-Vowel Families**
- **Digraphs**
- **Sight Words**
- **Consonant-Vowel Families**
- **Capital and Lower Case Letters**
- **Plurals**
- **Two-Vowel Rule** (Long Vowels) **and Two-Vowel Families**
- **Reading Sentences**
- **The Reading Clues**
- **Rhyming**

PRACTICE CARDS

- **One-Vowel Families and Words Decks 3 and 5**
- **Two-Vowel Families and Words Decks 4 and 6**

PRE-READERS

After becoming adept at decoding with the reading clues, the student can practice reading with the first Series pre-readers and then Series II.

Continue the alphabet sounds. Name the picture. What sound does it start with? Trace the letter that makes that sound.

rabbit

starts with
ruh sound

r

snake

starts with
sss sound

s

telephone
pole

starts with
t sound

t

umbrella

starts with
ŭ sound

u

violin

starts with
vvv sound

v

wet water

starts with
wuh sound

W

X

x

makes the
ks sound

x

yawn

starts with
yuh sound

y

zipper

starts with
zzz sound

z

Name the picture. What sound does it start with? Circle the letter that makes that sound.

horse

(h)   t   g

dog

n   d   m

ranch

s   r   t

lamb

q   c   l

cowgirl

o   b   c

fox   Can you hear the **x** sound (**ks**) in fox?

r   x   s

Name the picture. What sound does it start with? Circle the letter that makes that sound.

question mark

q   p   d

wet

f   w   z

jellyfish

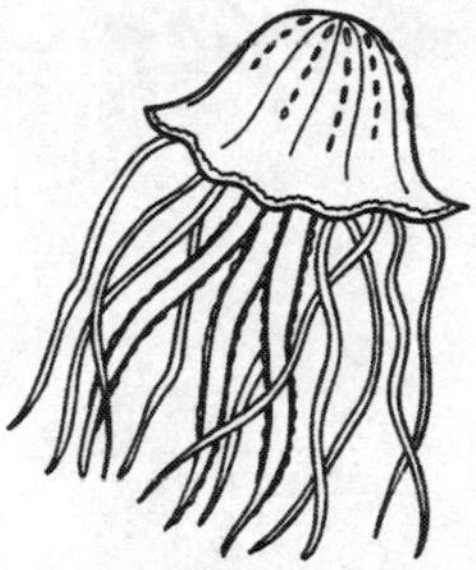

j   k   i

salt

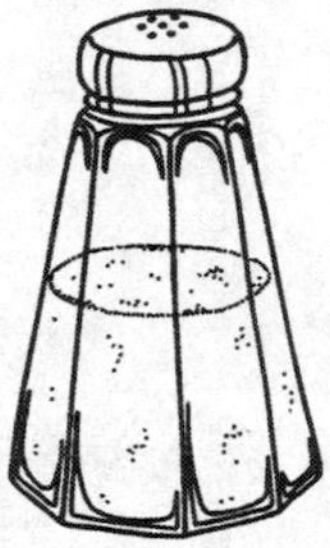

p   j   s

octopus

o   v   y

net

n   w   l

Name the letter. What sound does it make? Circle the picture that starts with that sound.

elephant
snake

s

dog
popcorn

p

moon
alligator

m

feather
girl

g

eggs
zipper

z

kangaroo
telephone

k

Name the letter. What sound does it make? Draw a line to the picture that starts with that sound.

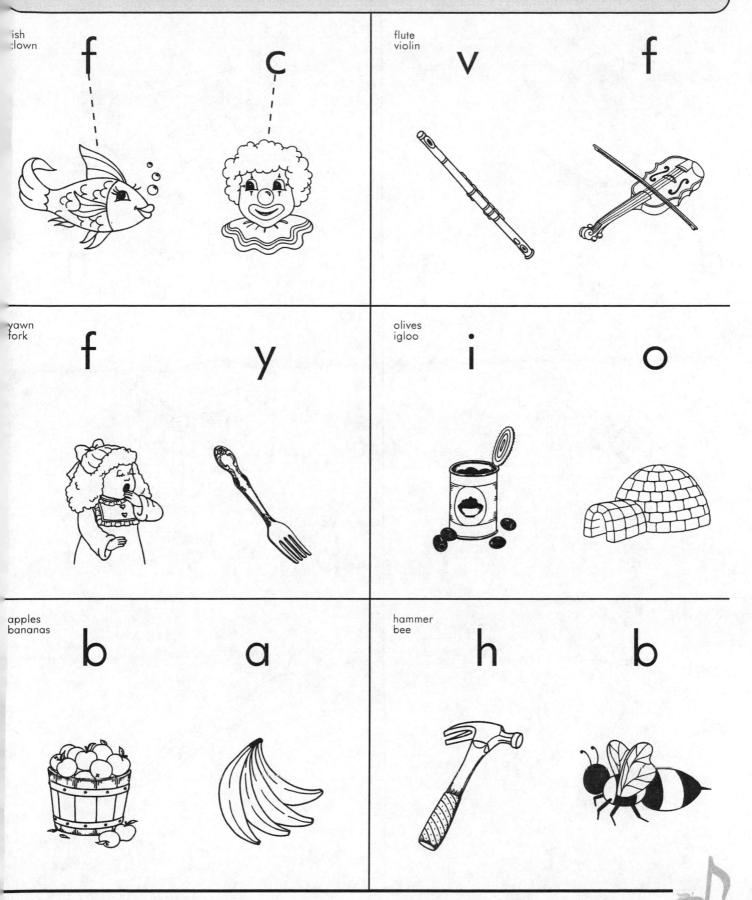

fish
clown

f   c

flute
violin

v   f

yawn
fork

f   y

olives
igloo

i   o

apples
bananas

b   a

hammer
bee

h   b

Name the picture. What sound does it start with? Draw a line from the picture to the letter that makes that sound.

doll

d   p   q   v   e   n

eggs

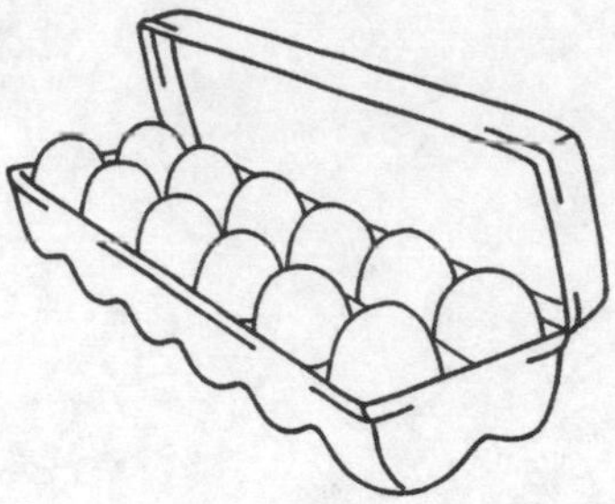

ant

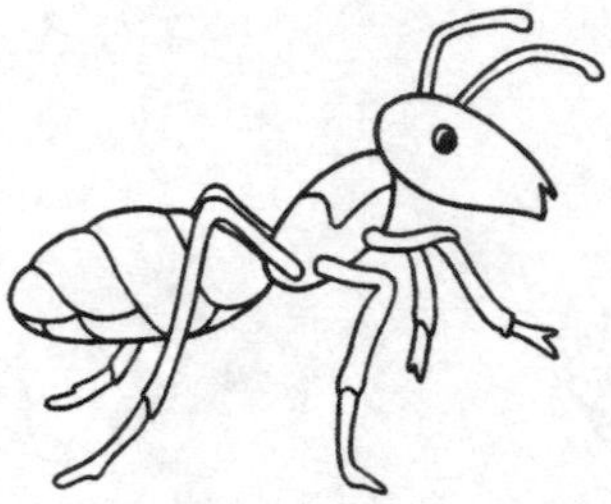

a   l   r   b   s   t

table

mouse

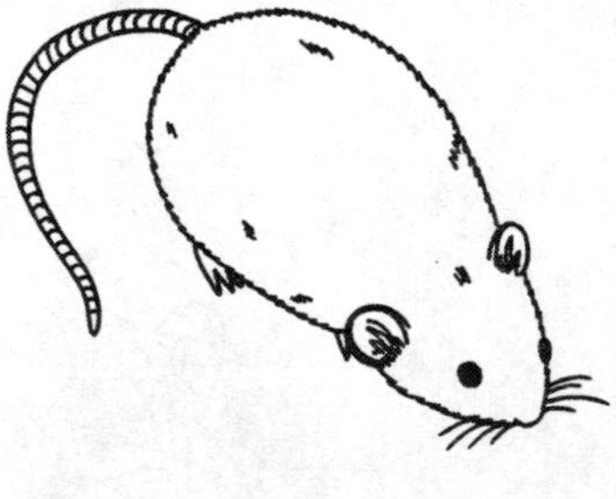

i   m   f   w   a   u

umbrella

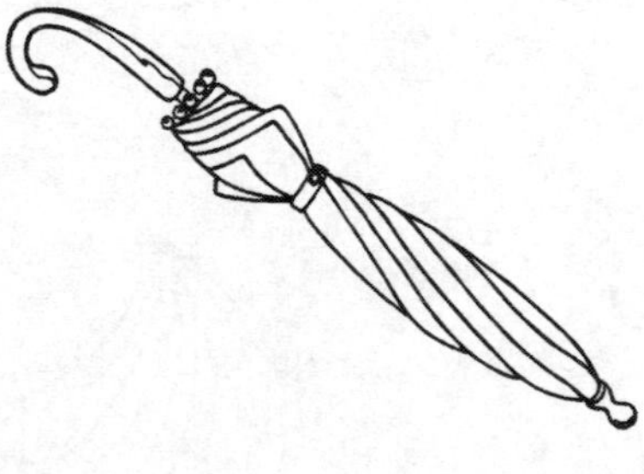

TIPS FOR THE PARENT

The vowels are Power Letters because they can say two sounds. Volume 2 teaches the vowels and the vowel rules.

THE VOWELS

The vowels are the keys to word attack skills (sometimes called decoding or sounding out) and spelling skills. A reader must have a solid, working knowledge of how to determine which sounds the vowels make in various words or syllables.

THE FIVE POWER LETTERS

Blending One-Vowel Words

(1) Review the One-Vowel Rule before you start.

(2) "Let's blend this word. First, how many vowels? One! That's correct. What is the vowel? Letter a! Yes! Now, when there's one vowel in the word it makes the short sound. So a will say a. Now let's blend the word caaap. Very good! Can you find the picture of a cap? Super! Circle it. Trace the vowel with your pencil."

(3) Continue for each word, moving from left to right.

(4) To review any difficult issues practice with the applicable cards and songs.

PRACTICE CARDS

Practice cards help students build spelling and reading fluency. Students acquire sight reading skills as they learn to instantly identify vowel families.

FOR THE CONCEPT:	PRACTICE WITH:
One-Vowel Words	One-Vowel Families Practice Cards One-Vowel Family Ride Song
Blending One-Vowel Words	Word Practice Cards (Blue Set) Blending Polka Song
Blending Consonant Vowel Words	Word Practice Cards (Blue Set) Ba-Be-Bi-Bo-Bu Song

at   un

p ig

met   doll

♪ Five Power Letters ♪

One day as I was reading,
With letters and their sounds,
Five of them jumped out at me,
And began to dance around.

"We are the Five Power Letters,
A - E - I - O - U !
We say not one, but two sounds.
Long and short for you."

I said, "I have a problem.
In a syllable or word,
A - E - I - O - U ! a - e - i - o - u,
Which sound should be heard?"

"When there's only one vowel
In a syllable or word,
We usually say the short sound,
a - e - i - o - u . . . as in

cat pen kiss fox hug!

In little words with two vowels,
The first vowel says its name.
Its name is called 'the long sound,'
And you say it just the same . . . as in

cake seal bike boat flute!

The second vowel helps the first to speak,
It cannot make one peep.
The second vowel helps the first to say its name,
And then it falls asleep!

We are the Five Power Letters,
A - E - I - O - U !
We say, not one, but two sounds.
Long and short for you.

We are the Five Power Letters,
A - E - I - O - U !
That's A - a,
      E - e,
        I - i,
          O - o ,
            U . . . uh!"

Five Power Letters

ā and ă   ē and ĕ   ī and ĭ

a   e   i   o   u

ō and ŏ   ū and ŭ

These are the Five Power Letters. Name the pictures. Draw a line from the picture to the correct beginning vowel sound. Trace the macron above the long vowels. Trace the breve above the short vowels.

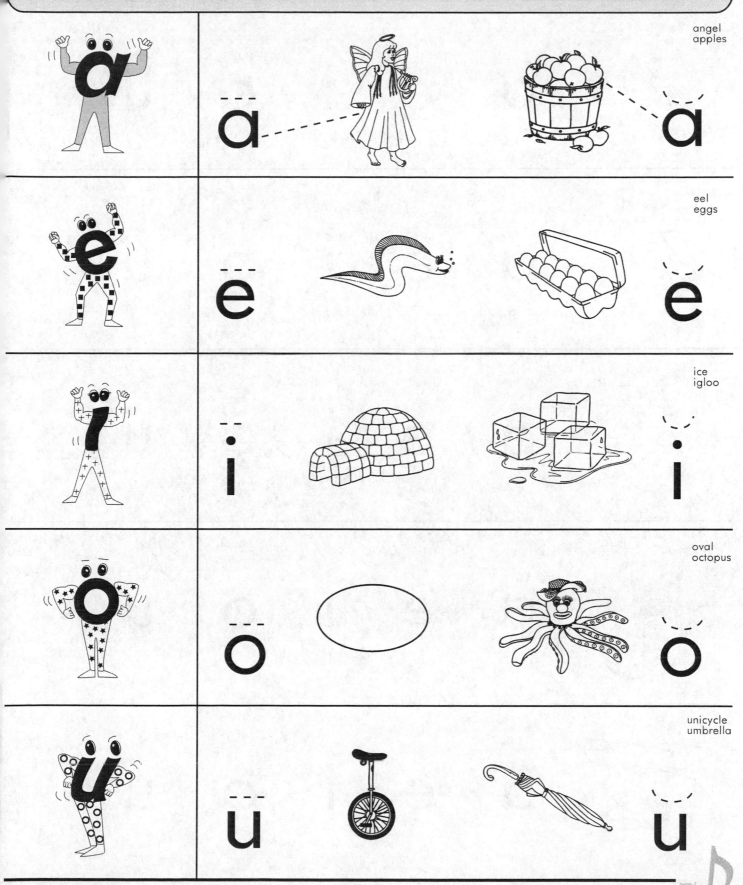

angel
apples

eel
eggs

ice
igloo

oval
octopus

unicycle
umbrella

Vowels - Long and Short   17

Name the picture. What sound does it start with? Name the vowels and their short sounds. Draw a circle around the letter that is the beginning sound of the picture.

   a e i o

   a e i o u

   a e i o u

   a e i o u

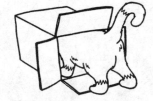   a e i o u

umbrella • ostrich • apple • elephant • in

Ike, the goat, likes pies. He also loves the vowels. Help Ike find the vowels and put a circle around each one.

Vowel Hunt

This is the Professor. He likes vowels. Vowels can say two sounds—long and short. Circle the vowels and color the Professor.

a b c d e f g h i j k l m n o p q r s t u v w x y z

Professor loves vowels.

This is Letter Lady. She likes the consonants. Consonants usually say only one sound.
Circle the consonants and color Letter Lady.

Letter Lady loves consonants.

Remember the words Letter Lady and Professor were arguing about in the video? Can we read words without consonants? Can we read words without vowels? Help the friends by tracing the correct vowel or consonant to complete each word.

b___g   b_a_g

___e___   n e t

p___p

___u___

pup

Miss Becky couldn't get Baby A to sleep. She called her friends to help her. Read the word they spelled for Miss Becky.

Miss Becky

hum

Circle the correct letter to answer each question.

What is the beginning (first) sound?

h u m

What is the ending (last) sound?

h u m

What is the middle sound?

h u m

Humming Hot Rod reminds us to keep our motor running as we blend letters to make words. Use your magic finger to blend hum.

hum

Humming Hot Rod

h u m

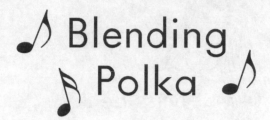

♪ Blending
Polka ♪

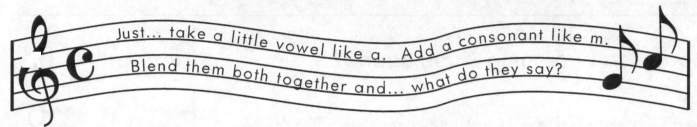

Just... take a little vowel like a. Add a consonant like m.
Blend them both together and... what do they say?

am, am, a-m says

"am !"

Am, am! Let's make a word.

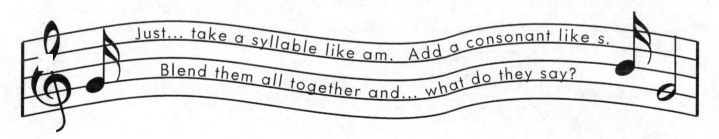

Just... take a syllable like am. Add a consonant like s.
Blend them all together and... what do they say?

Sam, Sam, S-a-m says

"Sam !"

♪ Sam! Sam! Do it again! ♪

Just... take a little vowel like **e**. Add a consonant like **t**.
Blend them both together and... what do they say?

et, et, e-t says

"et !"

Et!   Et! Let's make a word.

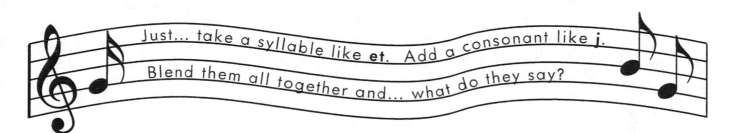

Just... take a syllable like **et**. Add a consonant like **j**.
Blend them all together and... what do they say?

jet, jet, j-e-t says

"jet !"

Jet!   Jet!   Do it again!

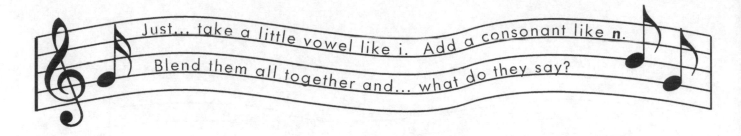

Just... take a little vowel like i. Add a consonant like **n**.
Blend them all together and... what do they say?

in, in, i-n says

"in !"

In!   In!   Let's make a word.

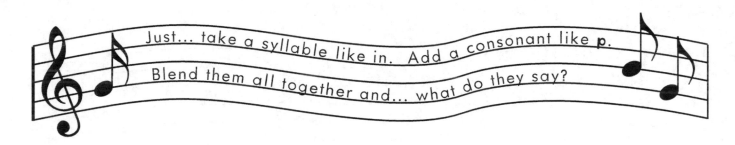

Just... take a syllable like in. Add a consonant like **p**.
Blend them all together and... what do they say?

pin, pin, p-i-n says

"pin !"

Pin!   Pin!   Do it again!

Try singing other letters and words in the song.

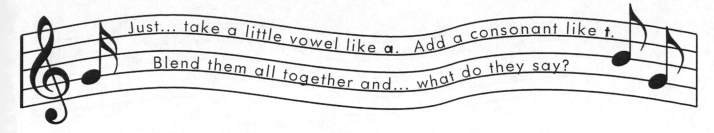

at, at, a-t says

"at !"

At!   At!   Let's make a word.

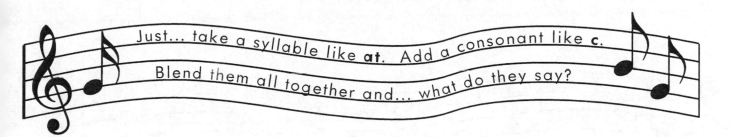

cat, cat, c-a-t says

"cat !"

Cat!   Cat!   Do it again!

Here are some different letters and words for the song.

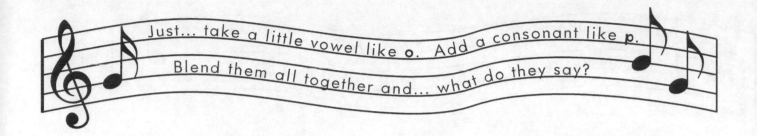

Just... take a little vowel like **o**. Add a consonant like **p**.
Blend them all together and... what do they say?

op, op, o-p says

"op !"

Op!   Op!   Let's make a word.

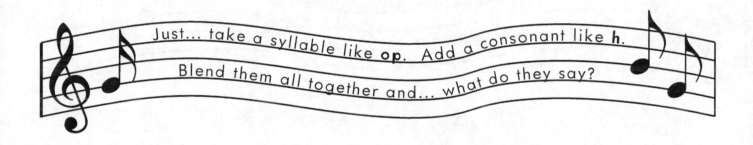

Just... take a syllable like **op**. Add a consonant like **h**.
Blend them all together and... what do they say?

hop, hop, h-o-p says

"hop !"

Hop!   Hop!   Do it again!

Here are some different letters and words for the song.

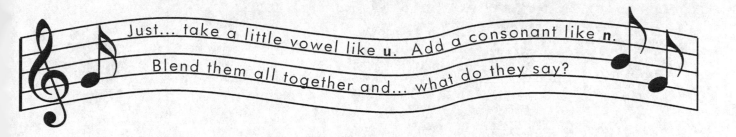

Just... take a little vowel like **u**. Add a consonant like **n**.
Blend them all together and... what do they say?

un, un, u-n says

"un !"

Un!   Un!   Let's make a word.

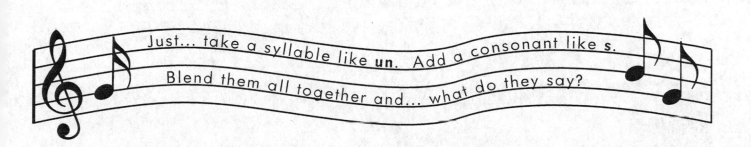

Just... take a syllable like **un**. Add a consonant like **s**.
Blend them all together and... what do they say?

sun, sun, s-u-n says

"sun !"

Sun!   Sun!   Do it again!

When there's only one vowel

In a syllable or word,

We usually say the short sound,

a - e - i - o - u . . . as in -

cat   pen

kiss   fox   hug

Remember Letter Lady and the Professor arguing about blending? See if you can read their words! Draw a line from the word to the picture it describes.

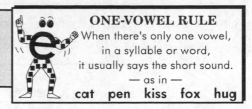

big

bug

bag

net

pup

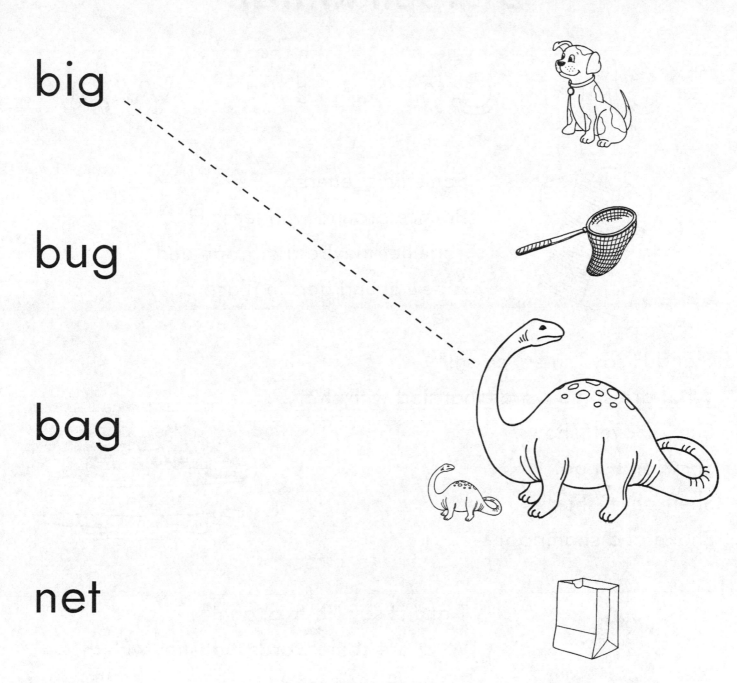

Digraph Riffrap

Some little letters
Bounce around with letter H.
Together they're a digraph and
A new sound gets in place.

S and H say "sh-sh sh-sh!"
What are some words that start with sh?
Ship, shovel, show . . .
Short and shoe.
Shell, shirt, shush . . .
Shake and shampoo!

T and H say "th-th and th!"
What are some words that start with th?
Think, third, thread . . .
Thistle and thumb.
Thin, thong, thermometer . . .
Thunder and thump!

This, than, that . . .

The and then.

There, those, theirs . . .

They and them!

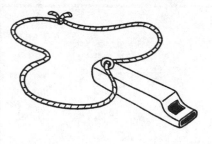

W and H say "wh-wh wh-wh!"

What are some words that start with wh?

While, whisper, whoop!

Whopper of a whale.

Where, whirl, wheel . . .

White and whistle!

C and H say "ch-ch ch-ch!"

What are some words that start with ch?

Channel, cherry, chin . . .

Chair and cha-cha.

Chatter, chimney, chess . . .

Cheese and chocolate!

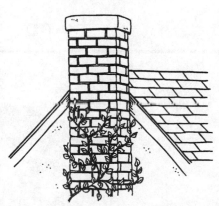

Digraphs are a single speech sound made by two letters. The most common are shown below. Trace the digraphs.

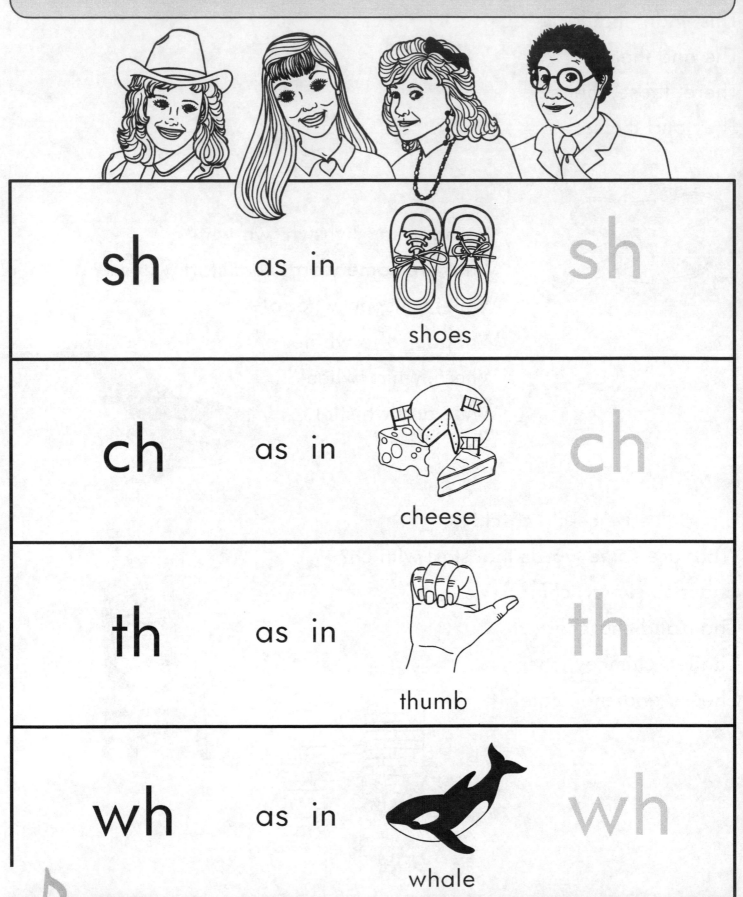

sh   as in   shoes   sh

ch   as in   cheese   ch

th   as in   thumb   th

wh   as in   whale   wh

Help Letter Lady. Circle the pictures that start with **sh**. Put an X on the pictures that do not start with **sh**.

sheep • thistle • shovel • shirt • shoes • shark • ship

Help Miss Becky. Circle the pictures that start with **th**. Put an X on the pictures that do not start with **th**.

th

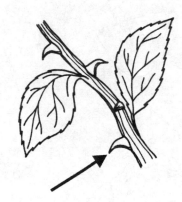

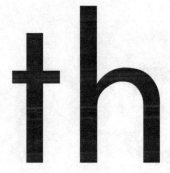

thistle • thermos • shoes • whistle • thumb • thorn • thermometer

Help Cowgirl Cory. Circle the pictures that start with **wh**. Put an X on the pictures that do not start with **wh**.

whiskers • whip • wheel • chain • whale • whistle • wheelbarrow

Digraphs 37

Help the Professor. Circle the pictures that start with **ch**. Put an X on the pictures that do not start with **ch**.

chain • chimpanzee • cheese • chair • cherries • shirt • chimney

(sh)   th   wh   ch

sh   th   wh   ch

sh   th   wh   ch

sh   th   wh   ch

sh   th   wh   ch

Sing along with the audio or video tape. Can you read the one-vowel families?
Color Cowgirl Cory.

One-Vowel Family Ride

Yip-ee-ki-yay! Yip-ee-ki-yo! As I ride around the country,
I take my one-vowel family along, and sing the one-vowel song.

ab	ack	ad	af
ag	al	am . . .	
an	ap	as	at

eb	eck	ed	ef
eg	el	em . . .	
en	ep	es	et
ev	ex	ez !	

ib   ick   id   if
ig   il   im...
in   ip   is   it
iv   ix   iz!

ob   ock   od   of
og   ol   om...
on   op   os   ot
ov   ox   oz!

ub   uck   ud   uf
ug   ul   um...
un   up   us   ut
uv   ux   uz!

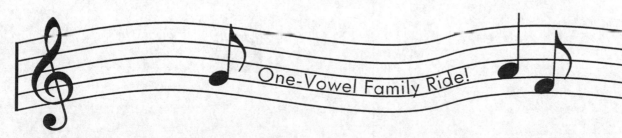

One-Vowel Family Ride!

One-Vowel Family Ride Song

Circle the one-vowel word family that will make the word.
Repeat the one-vowel rule.

man

(an)

am

m

cap

an

ap

c

rat

at

ub

r

bag

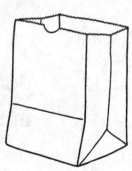

ag

us

b

Circle the one-vowel word family that will make the word.
Repeat the one-vowel rule.

ed

(**ed**)

em

b

ten

an

en

t

net

ep

et

n

vet

et

ot

v

Circle the one-vowel word family that will make the word.
Repeat the one-vowel rule.

pig

(ig)

ib

p

bib

ib

in

b

dig

ig

id

d

lip

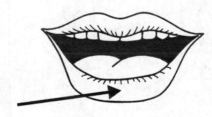

im

ip

l

Circle the one-vowel word family that will make the word.
Repeat the one-vowel rule.

dog

og

om

d

fox

og

ox

f

rod

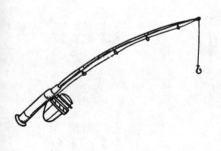

od

op

r

pot

ob

ot

p

Circle the one-vowel word family that will make the word.
Repeat the one-vowel rule.

bun

un

ut

b

tub

un

ub

t

sub

ub

un

s

mug

um

ug

m

Blend the word. Circle the picture that the word describes.
Trace the letter. Repeat the one-vowel rule.

cat
Sissy Snake

c a t

cot
bird

c o t

monkey
cab

c a b

game
can

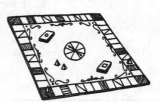 

c a n

cub
lip

c u b

cut
jam

c u t

Blend the word. Circle the word that describes the picture. Follow the arrows and trace the letter. Repeat the one-vowel rule.

ad

 mad   dad

ed

bed   red

ig

rig   pig

in

pin   win

Blend the word. Circle the word that describes the picture.
Repeat the one-vowel rule.

ot	hot	dot
op	stop	pop
ug	mug	rug
up	cup	pup

Blend the word. Circle the picture that the word describes.
Trace the letter. Repeat the one-vowel rule.

win
pin

w i n

wig
pig

w i g

sack
yak

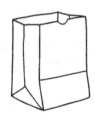 

y a k

man
van

v a n

vet
jet

v e t

dig
zig zag

z i g   z a g

Blend the word. Circle the picture that the word describes.
Trace the letter. Repeat the one-vowel rule.

hut
hug

h ut

hill
hat

h at

ten
hen

h en

jug
jump

j ug

jet
wet

j et

lamb
jam

j am

Draw a line from the beginning letter to the one-vowel word family that will make the word. Repeat the one-vowel rule.

duck

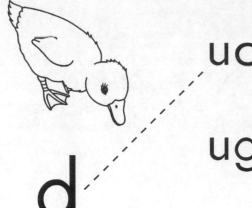

uck

ug

d

dot

•

ot

at

d

tub

ub

ob

t

sun

um

un

s

sub

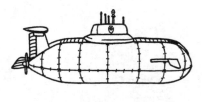

ab

ub

s

pot

ot

at

p

52

Blending One-Vowel Words

Challenger Phonics Fun, Volume 2

What sound does the letter make? Name the pictures. Draw a line from the pictures to the one-vowel families that are in the words.

cap
cup

c

up   ap

bug
bat

b

ug   at

mop
man

m

ap   an

rat
rug

r

ug   at

bag
bus

b

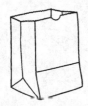 

us   ag

cat
cub

c

at   ub

© 2003 The Learning Crew

Blending One-Vowel Words   53

Blend the word. Can you hear the middle (vowel) sound?
Circle the picture that the word describes. Trace the vowel.
Repeat the one-vowel rule.

pie
pen

p e n

bat
bed

b e d

ten
tie

t e n

win
wet

w e t

newspaper
net

n e t

fed
fish

f e d

Blend the word. Can you hear the middle (vowel) sound?
Circle the picture that the word describes. Trace the vowel.
Repeat the one-vowel rule.

dolphin
dig

d i g

lid
lip

l i p

kick
kite

k i c k

bat
bib

b i b

pie
pig

p i g

film
fish

f i s h

Blending One-Vowel Words

Blend the word. Can you hear the middle (vowel) sound?
Circle the picture that the word describes. Trace the vowel.
Repeat the one-vowel rule.

cot
corn

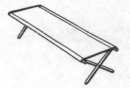

c o t

frog
fox

f o x

door
dog

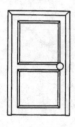 

d o g

hop
pop

h o p

rod
rice

r o d

pencil
pot

p o t

56 **Blending One-Vowel Words**

Blend the word. Can you hear the middle (vowel) sound?
Circle the picture that the word describes. Trace the vowel.
Repeat the one-vowel rule.

sun
sock

s u n

boat
bun

b u n

mug
moon

   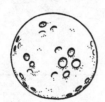

m u g

bed
bug

   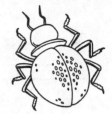

b u g

sit
sub

   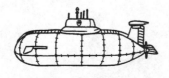

s u b

tub
turtle

t u b

I	the	a	is
here	no	my	

Is this Tag ?

(no)

yes

The dog is fun.

no

yes

I am on Tag.

no

yes

Read the sentences about Cowgirl Cory and her friends. Underline the sight words that we have learned. Circle the correct answer.

A ranch is fun.		no yes
Here is my pal, Tag.		no yes
Is Tag a dog?		no yes
This is my dog.		no yes

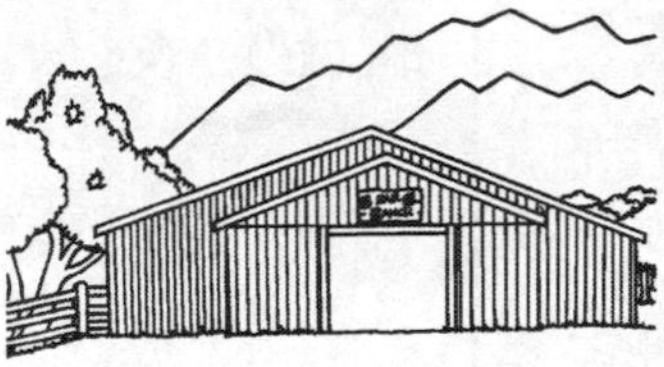

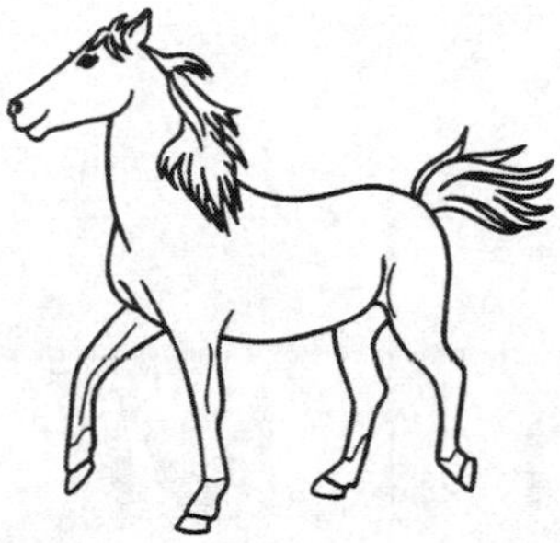

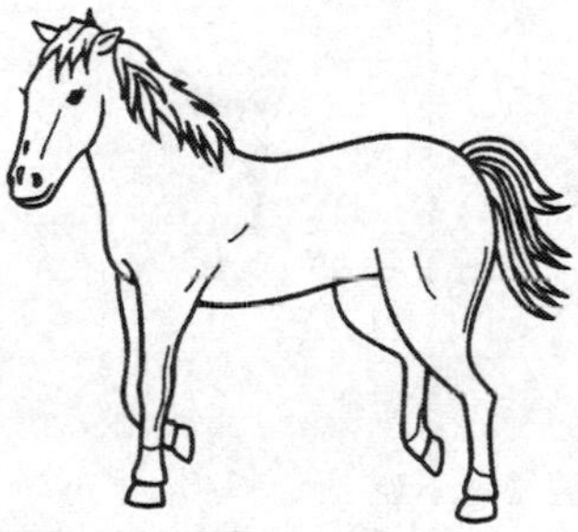

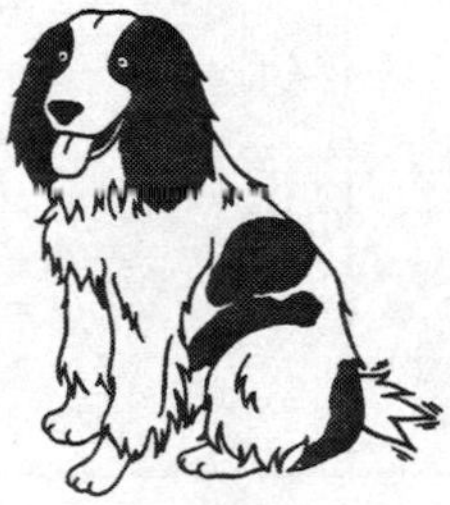

A   f   C   e   D   g

F   l   H   c   G   k

B   a   M   h   I   d

L   b   E   m   K   i

                                     J   j

Aa Bb Cc Dd Ee Ff Gg Hh Ii Jj Kk Ll Mm

N   r   V   p   O   o

R   s   Z   v   Q   u

S   y   P   w   U   t

Y   n   W   z   T   q

Nn Oo Pp Qq Rr Ss Tt Uu Vv Ww Xx Yy Zz

♪ Ba Be Bi Bo Bu ♪

Ba be bi bo bu   Ta te ti to tu
With the Ba be bi bo bu, we can read with speed!

ba	be	bi	bo	bu
ca	ke	ki	co	cu
da	de	di	do	du
fa	fe	fi	fo	fu

fat cat digs   mad fish jumps . . .   duck in a pan
. . . in a cup

ga	ge	gi	go	gu
ha	he	hi	ho	hu
ja	je	ji	jo	ju
la	le	li	lo	lu

ma	me	mi	mo	mu
na	ne	ni	no	nu
pa	pe	pi	po	pu
ra	re	ri	ro	ru

sun in a
bed . . .

Pat Pig in
mud

hot
dog
jig

hat
on a
rat

. . . on a rug

sa	se	si	so	su
ta	te	ti	to	tu
va	ve	vi	vo	vu
wa	we	wi	wo	wu

bad	bed	bid	bod	bud
cat	ket	kit	cot	cut
daf	def	dif	dof	duf
fan	fen	fin	fon	fun !

gap	gep	gip	gop	gup
hag	heg	hig	hog	hug
jan	jen	jin	jon	jun
lam	lem	lim	lom	lum !

mat	met	mit	mot	mut
nab	neb	nib	nob	nub
paf	pef	pif	pof	puf
rab	reb	rib	rob	rub !

mutt on a mat

hop and pop

kid in a bag

frog on a log

sal	sel	sil	sol	sul
tap	tep	tip	top	tup
van	ven	vin	von	vun
wat	wet	wit	wot	wut !

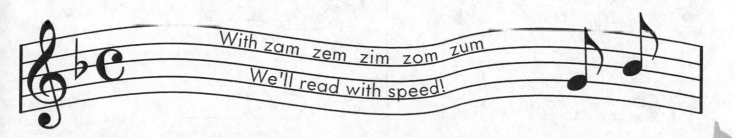

With zam zem zim zom zum
We'll read with speed!

Blend the word. Circle the letter that will end the word correctly. Repeat the one-vowel rule.

cup

(p)

t

cu___

pup

g

p

pu___

pop

n

p

po___

rat

t

m

ra___

net

t

b

ne___

cat

n

t

ca___

Blend the word. Circle the letter that will end the word correctly. Repeat the one-vowel rule.

hen

n

g

he___

man

t

n

ma___

pen

n

m

pe___

Tag

g

m

Ta___

wig

j

g

wi___

bug

g

n

bu___

Blend the word. Circle the letter that will end the word correctly. Repeat the one-vowel rule.

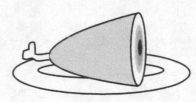
jam

m

x

ja___

ham

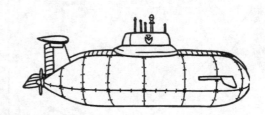

z

m

ha___

mug

m

g

mu___

sub

b

n

su___

tub

b

t

tu___

cab

t

b

ca___

Blend the word. Circle the letter that will end the word correctly. Repeat the one-vowel rule.

pan

d

n

pa___

pin

n

t

pi___

bed

n

d

be___

jet

p

t

je___

can

n

p

ca___

cub

t

b

cu___

Blending Consonant-Vowel Words

Name the picture. Blend the words. Circle the word that describes the picture.

pig   pit

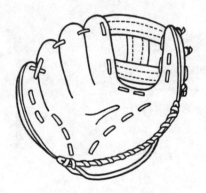

mitt   miss

cab   can

Name the picture. Blend the words. Circle the word that describes the picture.

jet   jem

bed   bug

cup   cub

Max, the Dog

This is Max, a cat.

No! Max is not a cat!

Max is a dog!

But Max can run fast.

Name the picture. Read the sentence. Circle the correct word that answers the sentence correctly.

Max is a log.

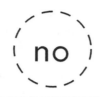 no   yes

Max is a cat.

no   yes

Is Max a dog?

no   yes

Is Max a cat?

no   yes

Here is the dog.

Here is the hat.

Here is a man.

Here is a bed.

This is a mop.

This is a bug.

This is a duck.

This is a bag.

Here is a pig.

no

yes

Here is a dog.

no

yes

Here is a bat.

no

yes

Here is a hat.

no

yes

Is my cat here ?

no

yes

Here is my dog.

no

yes

My dog is here.

no

yes

Here is my cat.

no

yes

Read the sentences.
Color the picture. Draw a sun in the sky.

Tag

This is Tag.

I am on Tag.

Here is my pal, Tag.

Read a Story with One-Vowel Sentences

Read the sentences.
Color the picture. Draw apples on the tree.

Is this Tag?

No. This is my dog, Max.

The dog is fun.

A ranch is fun.

Read a Story with One-Vowel Sentences

Tag can _____.

hum   run   pun

Max can run _____.

mast   jast   fast

Max will_____.

sun   run   sit

This is a _____.

Max   cat   dog

TIPS FOR THE PARENT

The vowels are called Power Letters because they can say two sounds—long and short.

Blending Two-Vowel Words

1 Review the Two-Vowel Rule before you start.

2 "Let's read this word using the two-vowel rule. How many vowels are in this word? What are the vowels? Which vowel will talk? The first vowel, letter i! Well done! What will the i say? Its name! That's correct! Letter i will say the long sound, ī. Put a macron over the i. Very good."

3 "What about the second vowel, letter e? What will it say? Nothing? You are so smart! The second vowel helps the first one say its name. Then it goes to sleep. Put a line through letter e."

Look for the vowels. How many vowels? The first vowel will say its own name. Put a macron above it. The second vowel will say nothing. It goes to sleep. Cross it out. Read the word.

TWO-VOWEL RULE
In little words with two vowels, the first vowel says its name, and the second vowel falls asleep! — as in —
cake seal bike boat flute

bike

boat

sheep

rain

86 Reading Two-Vowel Words

Challenger Phonics Fun, Volume 2

4 Continue with rake, moving from left to right down the page.

MARKING THE VOWELS
(for pronunciation)

Long Sound
When a vowel says its long sound, we put a macron (‾) above it.

cōat

We cross out the second vowel because it says nothing.

Short Sound
When a vowel says its short sound, we put a breve (˘) above it.

cŏt

SIGHT WORDS

Words that do not adhere to the one- or two-vowel rules must be memorized. Because they must be recognized by sight, we refer to them as sight words. In Volume 3, the Challenger Phonics system puts many sight words into categories called "Irregular Vowel Families."

PRACTICE

As a reader obtains the ability to immediately recognize syllables, reading comprehension increases. When a student reads quickly and with comprehension, reading is a joy. In Volume 2, the student learns to apply vowel rules and instantly recognize syllables, so that reading becomes smooth and pleasurable. A confident, fluent reader is more likely to enjoy studying all other subjects. Practice with the cards and songs is essential for reading fluency.

PRACTICE CARDS:

See **Parent Guide**, Two-Vowel Rule

Decks 2, 3, 4, **add S card to make plural words**
Deck 6, **Two-Vowel Words**
Deck 10, **Sight Words**

Ollie Octopus and his friends are here to find the vowels. Help them find the vowels and draw a circle around each one.

Sing the Five Power Letters song with the audio or video. Can you say the Two-Vowel Rule?

83

In little words with two vowels,
The first vowel says its name.
Its name is called 'the long sound'
And you say it just the same . . . as in -

cake   seal   bike   boat   flute!

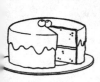

The second vowel helps the first to speak,
It cannot make one peep.
The second vowel helps the first to say its name,
And then it falls asleep!

Here are the short vowel words in the Five Power Letters song. Say the short vowel sounds. Trace the breves. Repeat the one-vowel rule. Can you read the words?

 as in căt

 as in pĕn

 as in kĭss

 as in fŏx

 as in hŭg

Here are the long vowel words in the Five Power Letters song. Say the long vowel sounds. Trace the macrons. Repeat the two-vowel rule. Can you read the words?

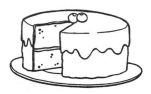

TWO-VOWEL RULE
In little words with two vowels, the first vowel says its name, and the second vowel falls asleep!
— as in —
cake   seal   bike   boat   flute

as in **cāke**

as in **sēal**

as in **bīke**

as in **bōat**

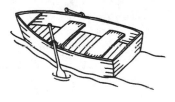

as in **flūte**

Add an **e** on the end to change the one-vowel words to two-vowel words.

 can

 can __e__

 pin

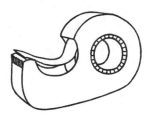 pin _____

 tap

 tap _____

 man

 man _____

Change the One-Vowel Words to Two-Vowel Words

Change each one-vowel word to a two-vowel word by adding the second vowel.

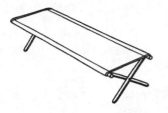 cot

 co_a_t

 ran

 ra_i_n

 bed

 be_a_d

 cut

 cut_e_

Change One-Vowel Words to Two-Vowel Words

Look for the vowels. How many vowels? The first vowel will say its own name. Put a macron above it. The second vowel will say nothing. It goes to sleep. Cross it out. Read the word.

bīke

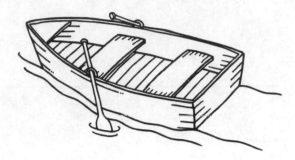

boat

sheep

rain

Look for the vowels. How many vowels? The first
vowel will say its own name. Put a macron above it.
The second vowel will say nothing. It goes to sleep.
Cross it out. Read the word.

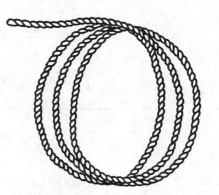

rōpè

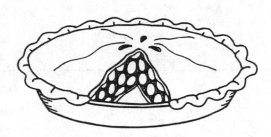

pie

whale

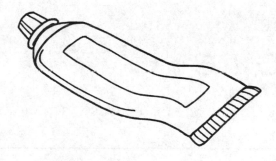

tube

TWO-VOWEL RULE

In little words with two vowels, the first vowel says its name, and the second vowel falls asleep!
— as in —

cake seal bike boat flute

t͞āp͟e̸

c o a t

s o a p

p i e

t i m e

Look for the vowels. How many vowels? The first vowel will say its own name. Put a macron above it. The second vowel will say nothing. It goes to sleep. Cross it out. Read the word.

k̄īte̷

lake

cape

feet

 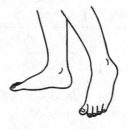

deer

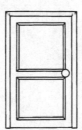 

TIPS FOR THE PARENT

The Reading Clues are a simple method for determining whether the vowels in words are long, short or silent.

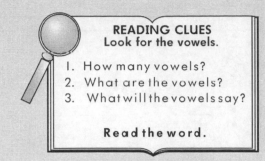

READING CLUES
Look for the vowels.

1. How many vowels?
2. What are the vowels?
3. What will the vowels say?

Read the word.

READING CLUES

The Reading Clues apply to whole words and to many syllables. They help the student decode unfamiliar words.

READING FLUENCY

When students can recognize word families like **am** and whole words like **lake**, let them read without sounding out the phonics. At this point, students are becoming fluent readers.

However, review phonics often and use the rules for decoding new words.

Words		Syllables	
can	cane	stam	- pede
Apply: One-Vowel Rule	Two-Vowel Rule	One-Vowel Rule	Two-Vowel Rule

1 "Look at the word. Can you find the vowels? How many vowels? One! Good job. Circle the number one. What is the vowel? Letter **a**! What will the letter **a** say? (There is only one vowel, so it will say the short sound, ă.) Let's mark the vowel with a breve. Now, let's read the word—**cat**! Great!"

2 "Let's find the vowels in this word. How many are there? Two! You are so smart. Circle the number two. What are the vowels? (Letters **o** and **a**!) Very good! So, what will the first vowel say? There are two vowels, so the first one says its name, right? (It says the long sound, ō.) What does the second vowel do? (It goes to sleep!) Let's put a macron over the vowel **o** and cross out the sleeping vowel **a**. Now let's read the word—**soap**! Yes! You are great!"

Reading Clues

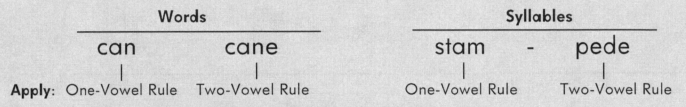

♪ Vowel Mystery ♪

There's a mystery
In every syllable and word.
Find and name the vowels,
That's the clue --
Which can be heard?

Count the power vowels,
To see if there are two.
Just follow the rules and
we'll know what to do!

The Detective found the Reading Clues! Follow the clues to help you read. When we know whether the vowel says its short or long sound, reading is easy!

can

① Circle the number of vowels that are in the word.

1   2

② What is the vowel?

a   e
i   o   u

③ What will the vowel say?

ā   ă

There is one vowel, so it will say the short sound, ă. Circle the correct vowel sound.

④ Read the word:

CHICKEN NOODLE

căn

The Detective found the Reading Clues! Follow the clues to help you read. When we know whether the vowel says its short or long sound, reading is easy!

c a n e

1 Circle the number of vowels that are in the word.

1   **2**

2 What are the vowels?

a   e

i   o   u

3 What will the vowels say?

ā   ă

There are two vowels, so the first vowel, **a**, will say its name - the long sound.
The second vowel, **e**, will go to sleep.
Circle the correct vowel sound.

4 Read the word:

c ā n e

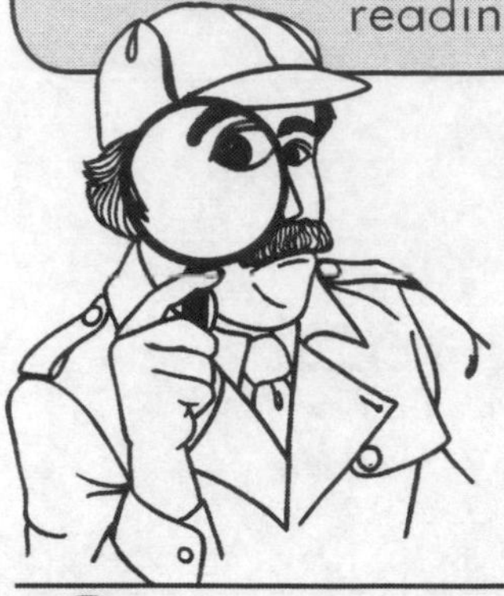

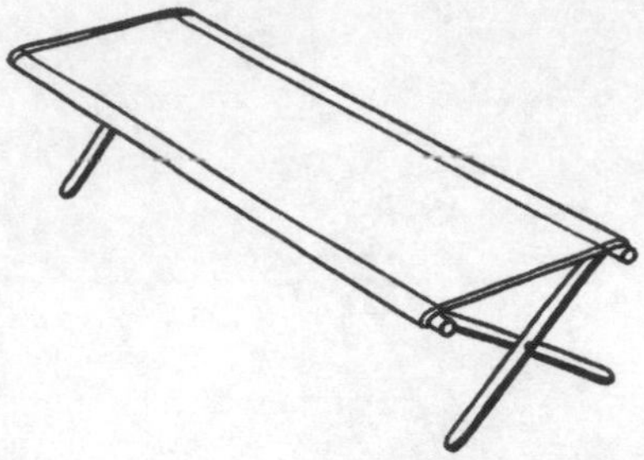

cot

1 Circle the number of vowels that are in the word.

1   2

2 What is the vowel?

a   e

i   o   u

3 What will the vowel say?

ō   ŏ

There is one vowel, so it will say the short sound, ŏ. Circle the correct vowel sound.

4 Read the word:

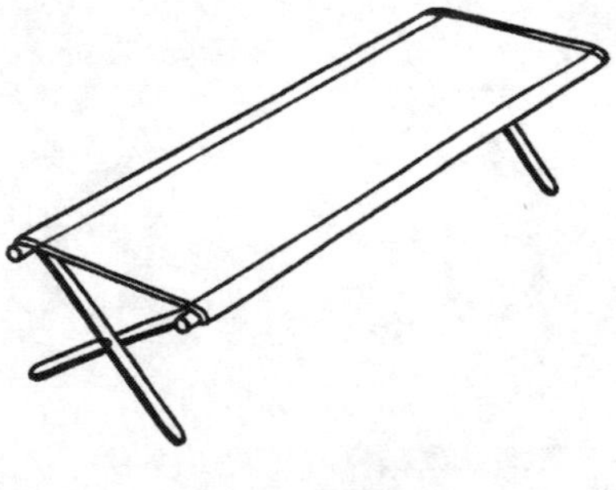

cot

The Detective found the Reading Clues! Follow the clues to help you read. When we know whether the vowel says its short or long sound, reading is easy!

coat

---

1 Circle the number of vowels that are in the word.

1    2

---

2 What are the vowels?

a   e

i   o   u

---

3 What will the vowels say?

  ō   ŏ

There are two vowels, so the first vowel, o, will say its name - the long sound.
The second vowel, a, will go to sleep. Circle the correct vowel sound.

---

4 Read the word:

coat

The Detective found the Reading Clues! Follow the clues to help you read. When we know whether the vowel says its short or long sound, reading is easy!

kit

① Circle the number of vowels that are in the word.

1   2

② What is the vowel?

a   e
i   o   u

③ What will the vowel say?

ī   ĭ

There is one vowel, so it will say the short sound, ĭ. Circle the correct vowel sound.

④ Read the word:

kit

The Detective found the Reading Clues! Follow the clues to help you read. When we know whether the vowel says its short or long sound, reading is easy!

kite

1 Circle the number of vowels that are in the word.

1   2

2 What are the vowels?

a   e

i   o   u

3 What will the vowels say?

ī   ĭ

There are two vowels, so the first vowel, **i**, will say its name - the long sound.
The second vowel, **e**, will go to sleep.
Circle the correct vowel sound.

4 Read the word:

kite

Use the Reading Clues to help read these words!

READING CLUES
Look for the vowels.
1. How many vowels?
2. What are the vowels?
3. What will the vowels say?
Read the word.

	Write a breve or macron above the vowel. Cross out sleeping vowels.	How many vowels?	Long or short?
	pĕn	1 / 2	short ⌣ / long —
	kīt̶e̶	1 / 2	short ⌣ / long —
	lĭd	1 / 2	short ⌣ / long —
	goat	1 / 2	short ⌣ / long —

Use the Reading Clues to help read these words!

READING CLUES
Look for the vowels.
1. How many vowels?
2. What are the vowels?
3. What will the vowels say?
Read the word.

	Write a breve or macron above the vowel. Cross out sleeping vowels.	How many vowels?	Long or short?
	cat	1 2	short ⌣ long —
	soap	1 2	short ⌣ long —
	flute	1 2	short ⌣ long —
	mane	1 2	short ⌣ long —

READING CLUES
Look for the vowels.
1. How many vowels?
2. What are the vowels?
3. What will the vowels say?
Read the word.

	Write a breve or macron above the vowel. Cross out sleeping vowels.	How many vowels?	Long or short?
	dog	1 2	short ⌣ long —
	pine	1 2	short ⌣ long —
	tree	1 2	short ⌣ long —
	mitt	1 2	short ⌣ long —

Use the Reading Clues to help read these words!

READING CLUES
Look for the vowels.
1. How many vowels?
2. What are the vowels?
3. What will the vowels say?
Read the word.

	Write a breve or macron above the vowel. Cross out sleeping vowels.	How many vowels?	Long or short?
	duck	1 2	short ⌣ long ─
	boat	1 2	short ⌣ long ─
	eel	1 2	short ⌣ long ─
	snake	1 2	short ⌣ long ─

The Reading Clues 103

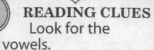

READING CLUES
Look for the vowels.
1. How many vowels?
2. What are the vowels?
3. What will the vowels say?

tăp

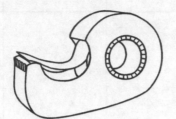

tāpe

cut

cute

mate

mat

shin

shine

fate

fat

rod

road

Read the words. Put a breve for a short vowel, or a macron for a long vowel. Cross out the sleeping vowel. Circle the word that describes the picture.

k ĭ t

(kīte)

c a n

c a n e

c a p e

c a p

m a n e

m a n

c o t

c o a t

b e a d

b e d

© 2003 The Learning Crew

One- and Two-Vowel Words   105

The puppets rhyme with rhythm! Rhyming words have the same sound in their ending syllables. Underline the syllables that rhyme. Circle the word that matches the picture.

(sun)   bun   seed   feed

pun   fun   weed   deed

run   need

Write **your** name.

_____

- -

same   name   sop   hop

tame   lame   mop   bop

jame   stop!

sun • name   weed • mop

Circle the words that rhyme.

  (hop)   fat   (pop)

 feed   seed   run

 sun   run   sit

 fan   game   man

 bun   stop   fun

hop • feed • sun • fan • bun

Read the word. If it is plural, circle the picture that has more than one. If it is not plural, circle the picture that has only one.

dogs

can

beds

bat

jugs

bugs

Circle the word that is correct for the picture. If there is more than one, circle the word that is plural. If there is only one, circle the word that is not plural (singular).

cane   canes   coat   coats

ɔine   pines   snake   snakes

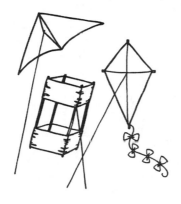

kite   kites   cake   cakes

Circle the vowel that is missing in the word. Write the vowel in the lines. Mark the vowel with the macron. Cross out the vowel that goes to sleep.

a

(o)

g͞o͞at

a

e

b__e

e

a

ch__in

u

a

c__te

a

i

r__ke

i

o

d__me

Circle the vowel that is missing in the word. Write the vowel in the lines. Mark the vowel with the macron. Cross out the vowel that goes to sleep.

o
i

p__ne

a
o

c__ke

u
o

c__at

a
i

h__ve

u
i

fl__te

e
o

__el

Reading Two-Vowel Words   111

Two-Vowel Rag

If you want to be a reader, 'cause you know it makes a leader, Come along with me and my two-vowel family!

abe	ace	ade	afe
ake	ale	ame	ane
ape	ate	ave	

That's a two-vowel family!

ebe	ece	ede	eef
eek	eel	eme	ene
eep	eet	eve	

That's a two-vowel family!

ibe	ice	ide	ife
ike	ile	ime	ine
ipe	ite	ive	

That's a two-vowel family!

obe	oce	ode	oaf
oke	ole	ome	one
oap	oat	ove	

That's a two-vowel family!

ube	uce	ude	ufe
uke	ule	ume	une
upe	ute	uve	

That's a two-vowel family!

That's a two-vowel, that's a two-vowel,
That's a two-vowel family!

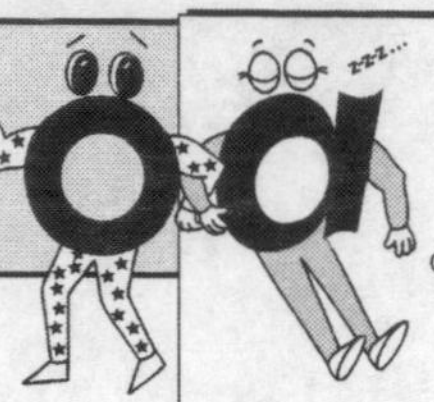

TWO-VOWEL RULE

In little words with two vowels, the first vowel says its name, and the second vowel falls asleep!
— as in —

cake seal bike boat flute

oat

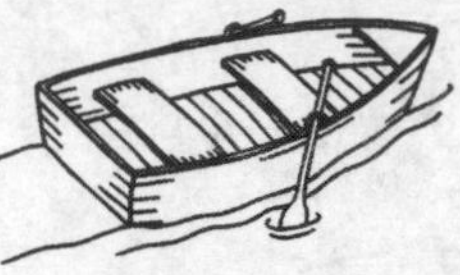

coat   (boat)

ite

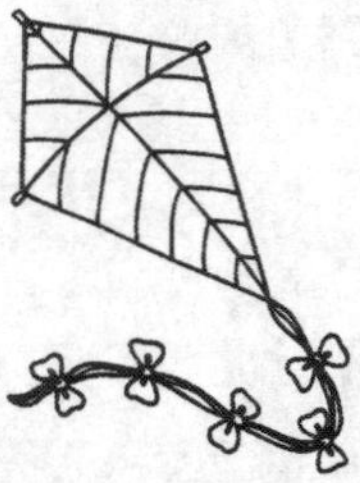

bite   kite

une

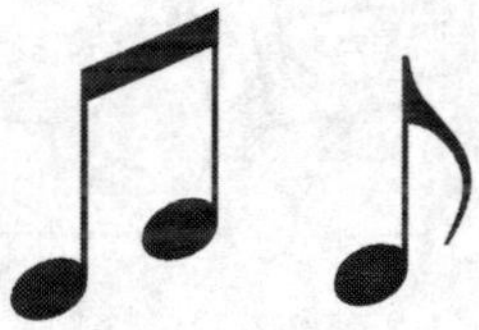

tune   June

ake

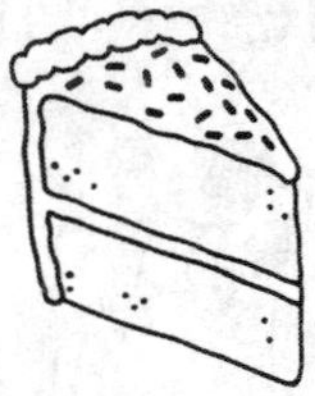

cake   bake

eel

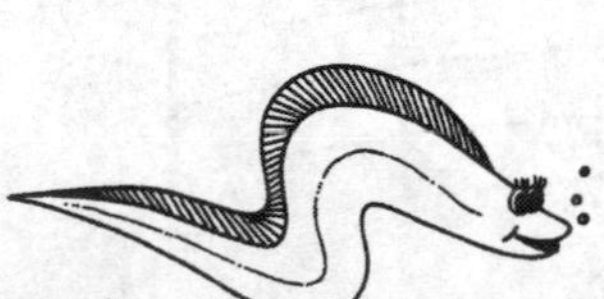

heel   eel

Read the two-vowel family words. In each section,
circle the word that names the picture.

ane

lane   (mane)

eed

need   weed

ide

side   ride

one

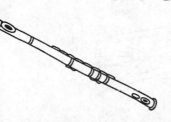

bone   cone

ute

mute   flute

Two-Vowel Word Families

TWO-VOWEL RULE
In little words with two vowels, the first vowel says its name, and the second vowel falls asleep!
— as in —
cake seal bike boat flute

See the bike.

See the dime.

See the flute.

See the gate.

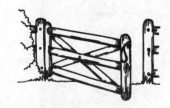

See the grapes.

TWO-VOWEL RULE
In little words with two vowels, the first vowel says its name, and the second vowel falls asleep!
— as in —
cake seal bike boat flute

This is a lake.

Here is a pie.

See the chain.

This is a rake.

This is a rake.

Here is a tree.

Here is a boat.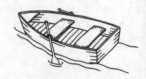

See the whales.

Here is a rope.

See the snails.

Here is a seal.

TWO-VOWEL RULE

In little words with two vowels, the first vowel says its name, and the second vowel falls asleep! — as in —

cake seal bike boat flute

This is a whale.

(no)

yes

The rope is here.

no

yes

Here are five sheep.

no

yes

This is a rake.

no

yes

Here is cake.

no

yes

TWO-VOWEL RULE
In little words with two vowels, the first vowel says its name, and the second vowel falls asleep! — as in —
cake seal bike boat flute

This is not a   toad
                    road

This is not a   leaf
                    leak

This is not   blue
                    glue

This is not a   chain
                    pain

This is not a   tie
                    pie

Use the Reading Clues as you read the sentence.
Circle the correct word for the sentence.

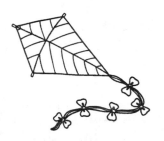	Here is a	wheel peel
	This is not a	kite tune
	This is a	tube tune
	Here is the	soap soak
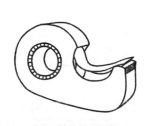	This is the	tape cape

My Ranch

Here I am with Tag.

I like Tag.

See Tag's tail?

Tag is tan.

I ride Tag.
Tag will lope!

I like Tag's mane.
Tag can back up,
   and Tag can spin!

This is Max.

Max and Tag run fast
    at the ranch!

Max can run fast.

Max can win this game.

It is fun with my dog
and my horse.

I brush Tag and Max.
Tag likes oats.

Max can eat oats.

Max can sit.

Is Max black and white?

Max wags his tail.

I love my horse and my dog!

Parent: The **ove** as in **love** does not conform to the two-vowel rule, so **love** is a sight word.

We Are Reading!

Professor Fiddle Fuddle

Miss Becky

Letter Lady

Gugenheimer

Bitsy

Detective

Granny Sight Word

Cowgirl Cory

Max

Tag